Author:
Pauline Chandler, M.S. Ed.

Illustrator:
Sue Fullam

Editors:
Christine Berner
Evan D. Forbes, M.S. Ed.
Walter Kelly, M.A.

Senior Editor:
Sharon Coan, M.S. Ed.

Art Direction:
Elayne Roberts

Product Manager:
Phil Garcia

Imaging:
Rick Chacón

Photo Cover Credit:
Images provided by
PhotoDisc ©1994

Publishers:
Rachelle Cracchiolo, M.S. Ed.
Mary Dupuy Smith, M.S. Ed.

Hands-On Minds-On Science

Ecology

Primary

Teacher Created Materials, Inc.
P.O. Box 1040
Huntington Beach, CA 92647
©1994 Teacher Created Materials, Inc.
Made in U.S.A.
ISBN-1-55734-633-X

WESTERN EDUCATIONAL ACTIVITIES LTD.
12006 - 111 Ave. Edmonton, Alberta T5G 0E2
Ph: (403) 413-7055 Fax: (403) 413-7056

Table of Contents

Table of Contents *(cont.)*

Introduction

What Is Science?

What is science to young children? Is it something that they know is a part of their world? Is it a textbook in the classroom? Is it a tadpole changing into a frog? A sprouting seed, a rainy day, a boiling pot, a turning wheel, a pretty rock, or a moonlit sky? Is science fun and filled with wonder and meaning? What is science to a child?

Science offers you and your eager students opportunities to explore the world around you, and make connections between the things you experience. The world becomes your classroom, and you, the teacher, a guide.

Science can, and should, fill children with wonder. It should cause them to be filled with questions and the desire to discover the answers to their questions. And, once they have discovered answers, they should be actively seeking new questions to answer.

The books in this series give you and the students in your classroom the opportunity to learn from the whole of your experience—the sights, sounds, smells, tastes, and touches, as well as what you read, write about, and do. This whole-science approach allows you to experience and understand your world as you explore science concepts and skills together.

What Is Ecology?

Ecology is the study of living and nonliving things and how they depend on and interact with one another for survival. By studying ecology, we are able to better understand life on our planet and how we are affected by environmental changes near and far.

Scientists will use a multitude of disciplines when studying the world around them. These disciplines include climatology, chemistry, computer science, geology, meteorology, mathematics, oceanography, physics, among others. Ecologists, who are people who study the environment, look at the world on three main levels: 1) populations, 2) communities, and 3) ecosystems. *Population* is defined as the number of species living in a given area at the same time. *Community* is defined as groups of plants and animals living together in the same environment. *Ecosystem* is defined as the combination of all living things in a community and its nonliving, or physical environment.

The Scientific Method

The "scientific method" is one of several creative and systematic processes for proving or disproving a given question, following an observation. When the "scientific method" is used in the classroom, a basic set of guiding principles and procedures is followed in order to answer a question. However, real world science is often not as rigid as the "scientific method" would have us believe.

This systematic method of problem solving will be described in the paragraphs that follow.

1   Make an OBSERVATION.

The teacher presents a situation, gives a demonstration, or reads background material that interests students and prompts them to ask questions. Or students can make observations and generate questions on their own as they study a topic.

Example: Water dripping from the inside of an apple.

2   Select a QUESTION to investigate.

In order for students to select a question for a scientific investigation, they will have to consider the materials they have or can get, as well as the resources (books, magazines, people, etc.) actually available to them. You can help them make an inventory of their materials and resources, either individually or as a group.

Tell students that in order to successfully investigate the questions they have selected, they must be very clear about what they are asking. Discuss effective questions with your students. Depending upon their level, simplify the question or make it more specific.

Example: Where do you find water in a food chain?

3   Make a PREDICTION (Hypothesis).

Explain to students that a hypothesis is a good guess about what the answer to a question will probably be. But they do not want to make just any arbitrary guess. Encourage students to predict what they think will happen and why.

In order to formulate a hypothesis, students may have to gather more information through research.

Have students practice making hypotheses with questions you give them. Tell them to pretend they have already done their research. You want them to write each hypothesis so it follows these rules:

1. It is to the point.
2. It tells what will happen, based on what the question asks.
3. It follows the subject/verb relationship of the question.

Example: I think there is water inside the apple.

The Scientific Method *(cont.)*

4 Develop a **PROCEDURE** to test the hypothesis.

The first thing students must do in developing a procedure (the test plan) is to determine the materials they will need.

They must state exactly what needs to be done in step-by-step order. If they do not place their directions in the right order, or if they leave out a step, it becomes difficult for someone else to follow their directions. A scientist never knows when other scientists will want to try the same experiment to see if they end up with the same results!

Example: Weighing, drying, and then weighing the apple again, will allow you to see a difference in the overall weight of the apple.

5 Record the **RESULTS** of the investigation in written and picture form.

The results (data collected) of a scientific investigation are usually expressed two ways—in written form and in picture form. Both are summary statements. The written form reports the results with words. The picture form (often a chart or graph) reports the results so the information can be understood at a glance.

Example: The results of the investigation can be recorded on a data-capture sheet provided (page 33).

6 State a **CONCLUSION** that tells what the results of the investigation mean.

The conclusion is a statement which tells the outcome of the investigation. It is drawn after the student has studied the results of the experiment, and it interprets the results in relation to the stated hypothesis. A conclusion statement may read something like either of the following: "The results show that the hypothesis is supported," or "The results show that the hypothesis is not supported." Then restate the hypothesis if it was supported or revise it if it was not supported.

Example: The hypothesis that stated "there is water inside the apple" is supported (or not supported).

7 Record **QUESTIONS, OBSERVATIONS,** and **SUGGESTIONS** for future investigations.

Students should be encouraged to reflect on the investigations that they complete. These reflections, like those of professional scientists, may produce questions that will lead to further investigations.

Example: What other foods contain water?

Science-Process Skills

Even the youngest students blossom in their ability to make sense out of their world and succeed in scientific investigations when they learn and use the science-process skills. These are the tools that help children think and act like professional scientists.

The first five process skills on the list below are the ones that should be emphasized with young children, but all of the skills will be utilized by anyone who is involved in scientific study.

Observing

It is through the process of observation that all information is acquired. That makes this skill the most fundamental of all the process skills. Children have been making observations all their lives, but they need to be made aware of how they can use their senses and prior knowledge to gain as much information as possible from each experience. Teachers can develop this skill in children by asking questions and making statements that encourage precise observations.

Communicating

Humans have developed the ability to use language and symbols which allow them to communicate not only in the "here and now" but also over time and space as well. The accumulation of knowledge in science, as in other fields, is due to this process skill. Even young children should be able to understand the importance of researching others' communications about science and the importance of communicating their own findings in ways that are understandable and useful to others. The ecology journal and the data-capture sheets used in this book are two ways to develop this skill.

Comparing

Once observation skills are heightened, students should begin to notice the relationships between things that they are observing. *Comparing* means noticing similarities and differences. By asking how things are alike and different or which is smaller or larger, teachers will encourage children to develop their comparison skills.

Ordering

Other relationships that students should be encouraged to observe are the linear patterns of seriation (order along a continuum: e.g., rough to smooth, large to small, bright to dim, few to many) and sequence (order along a time line or cycle). By making graphs, time lines, cyclical and sequence drawings, and by putting many objects in order by a variety of properties, students will grow in their abilities to make precise observations about the order of nature.

Categorizing

When students group or classify objects or events according to logical rationale, they are using the process skill of categorizing. Students begin to use this skill when they group by a single property such as color. As they develop this skill, they will be attending to multiple properties in order to make categorizations; the animal classification system, for example, is one system students can categorize.

Science-Process Skills (cont.)

Relating

Relating, which is one of the higher-level process skills, requires student scientists to notice how objects and phenomena interact with one another and the change caused by these interactions. An obvious example of this is the study of chemical reactions.

Inferring

Not all phenomena are directly observable, because they are out of humankind's reach in terms of time, scale, and space. Some scientific knowledge must be logically inferred based on the data that is available. Much of the work of paleontologists, astronomers, and those studying the structure of matter is done by inference.

Applying

Even very young, budding scientists should begin to understand that people have used scientific knowledge in practical ways to change and improve the way we live. It is at this application level that science becomes meaningful for many students.

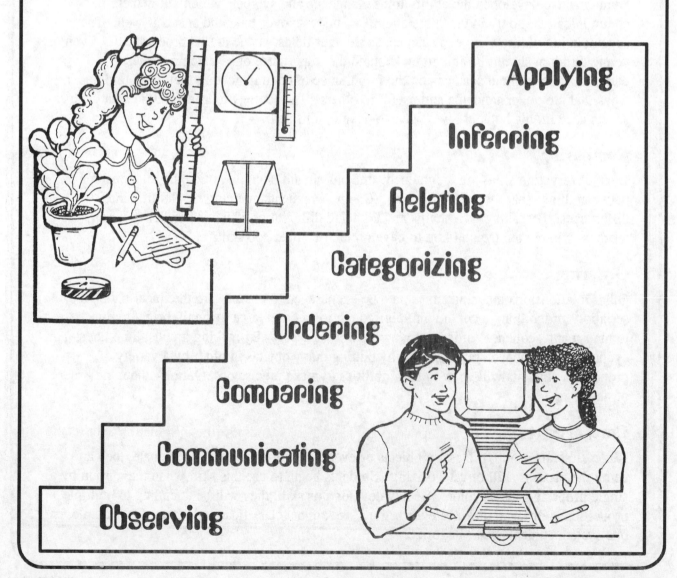

Applying

Inferring

Relating

Categorizing

Ordering

Comparing

Communicating

Observing

Organizing Your Unit

Designing a Science Lesson

In addition to the lessons presented in this unit, you will want to add lessons of your own, lessons that reflect the unique environment in which you live, as well as the interests of your students. When designing new lessons or revising old ones, try to include the following elements.

Question

Pose a question to your students that will guide them in the direction of the experience you wish to perform. Encourage all answers, but you want to lead the students towards the experiment you are going to be doing. Remember, there must be an observation before there can be a question. (Refer to The Scientific Method, pages 5-6.)

Setting the Stage

Prepare your students for the lesson. Brainstorm to find out what students already know. Have children review books to discover what is already known about the subject. Invite them to share what they have learned.

Materials Needed for Each Group or Individual

List the materials each group or individual will need for the investigation. Include a data-capture sheet when appropriate.

Procedure

Make sure students know the steps to take to complete the activity. Whenever possible, ask them to determine the procedure. Make use of assigned roles in group work. Create (or have your students create) a data-capture sheet. Ask yourself, "How will my students record and report what they have discovered? Will they tally, measure, draw, or make a checklist? Will they make a graph? Will they need to preserve specimens?" Let students record results orally, using a video or audio tape recorder. For written recording, encourage students to use a variety of paper supplies such as poster board or index cards. It is also important for students to keep a journal of their investigation activities. Journals can be made of lined and unlined paper. Students can design their own covers. The pages can be stapled or be put together with brads or spiral binding.

Extensions

Continue the success of the lesson. Consider which related skills or information you can tie into the lesson, like math, language arts skills, or something being learned in social studies. Make curriculum connections frequently and involve the students in making these connections. Extend the activity, whenever possible, to home investigations.

Closure

Encourage students to think about what they have learned and how the information connects to their own lives. Prepare ecology journals using directions on page 84. Provide an ample supply of blank and lined pages for students to use as they complete the Closure activities. Allow time for students to record their thoughts and pictures in their journals.

Organizing Your Unit *(cont.)*

Structuring Student Groups for Scientific Investigations

Using cooperative learning strategies in conjunction with hands-on and discovery learning methods will benefit all the students taking part in the investigation.

Cooperative Learning Strategies

1. In cooperative learning, all group members need to work together to accomplish the task.
2. Cooperative learning groups should be heterogenous.
3. Cooperative learning activities need to be designed so that each student contributes to the group and individual group members can be assessed on their performance.
4. Cooperative learning teams need to know the social as well as the academic objectives of a lesson.

Cooperative Learning Groups

Groups can be determined many ways for the scientific investigations in your class. Here is one way of forming groups that has proven to be successful in primary classrooms.

- **The Team Leader**—scientist in charge of reading directions and setting up equipment.
- **The Ecologist**—scientist in charge of carrying out directions (can be more than one student).
- **The Stenographer**—scientist in charge of recording all of the information.
- **The Transcriber**—scientist who translates notes and communicates findings.

If the groups remain the same for more than one investigation, require each group to vary the people chosen for each job. All group members should get a chance to try each job at least once.

Using Centers for Scientific Investigations

Set up stations for each investigation. To accommodate several groups at a time, stations may be duplicated for the same investigation. Each station should contain directions for the activity, all necessary materials (or a list of materials for investigators to gather), a list of words (a word bank) which students may need for writing and speaking about the experience, and any data-capture sheets or needed materials for recording and reporting data and findings.

Model and demonstrate each of the activities for the whole group. Have directions at each station. During the modeling session, have a student read the directions aloud while the teacher carries out the activity. When all students understand what they must do, let small groups conduct the investigations at the centers. You may wish to have a few groups working at the centers while others are occupied with other activities. In this case, you will want to set up a rotation schedule so all groups have a chance to work at the centers.

Assign each team to a station, and after they complete the task described, help them rotate in a clockwise order to the other stations. If some groups finish earlier than others, be prepared with another unit-related activity to keep students focused on main concepts. After all rotations have been made by all groups, come together as a class to discuss what was learned.

10

Just the Facts

Think about your community. Do you live in an urban, suburban, or rural community? What are the major components of your community? Brainstorm a list of all the parts of your community. Who lives in your community? What do they need to be able to survive in your community?

You will be learning about communities of plants and animals and how they live together. You will also be studying their environment. This study of the relationships between organisms (plants and animals) and their environment is the branch of science called *ecology*. While studying ecology, you will learn about ecosystems. An *ecosystem* is the combination of all living things in a community and its nonliving, or physical environment.

You will be learning about the interdependence of many organisms. It will be helpful if you understand that all living things need certain things to survive. They need the following:

- **WATER**—Water helps a plant make food and carries that food throughout the plant. Water also is essential for animals to survive.
- **OXYGEN** and **CARBON DIOXIDE**—Plants produce oxygen for animals to breathe. Animals exhale carbon dioxide which plants need to make food.
- **SUN**—The sun's light gives the leaves of plants the energy they need to make food. This energy is then passed along to animals that eat plants and then animals that eat plant eating animals. The sun's energy is in every living thing.
- **FOOD**—Food supplies animals with the energy they need to survive. Plants make their own food using the energy of the sun, but they also need nutrients from the soil. Many of those nutrients come from plants and animals that have decomposed.

All organisms can be placed in one of three categories: producers, consumers, or decomposers. These categories are defined below.

- **PRODUCERS**—Organisms that are able to produce their own food using energy from the sun. Examples: *algae, grass, orange trees.*
- **CONSUMERS**—Animals that eat other animals or plants. Examples: *giraffes, tigers, goldfish.*
- **DECOMPOSERS**—Organisms which are able to break down dead plants and animals into carbon, oxygen, and nitrogen so that these chemicals can be used again and again by plants and animals. Examples: *earthworms, bacteria, fungus.*

Being Connected

Question

What is an ecosystem?

Setting the Stage

- Survey the class to see how many students have heard the words *ecology* or *ecosystem*. Ask the class to define the words. Write student definitions on the board and save them.
- Explain to the class that they are going to discover the meaning of ecosystem by creating an ecosystem of their own.

Materials Needed for Each Group

- a set (one per student) of 3" x 5" (7.5 cm x 12.5 cm) index cards, individually labeled with key elements of an ecosystem (e.g., sun, grass, apple tree, mouse, rabbit, snake, hawk, fungus, earthworms, etc.)
- colored markers or crayons
- pins or tape
- large ball of yarn
- data-capture sheet (page 13), one per student

Procedure

1. Divide the class into groups of 8-11 students. Hand out the materials listed above to each group, making sure that every student has an element card.
2. Have each student decorate his/her card and pin or tape it to the front of his/her shirt.
3. Have each group stand in a circle.
4. An ecosystem starts with the sun. In each group, the student with the sun card should hold the ball of yarn. Explain that the sun gives energy to all living things.
5. While holding onto the end, have the sun pass the ball of yarn to a plant. The plant should hold onto the yarn and pass the ball to another plant, continuing in this way until all plants are holding onto the yarn.
6. Have students pass the yarn to the plant eaters, meat eaters, and finally the decomposers.
7. Discuss the relationship between the elements.
8. After the yarn has been passed to everyone, see if the students can now define the term *ecosystem*. Write the new definition on the board and compare it to their first one.
9. Introduce the terms *producer*, *consumer*, and *decomposer*. Have students group themselves by these categories.
10. Have each student complete a data-capture sheet.

Extensions

- Remove some key elements from the student groups and see what happens to the ecosystems.
- Have students write to national and local organizations that deal with ecology and protecting and defending ecosystems. Ask them to send literature about their organization.

Closure

In their ecology journals, have students write about the importance of ecosystems.

Being Connected *(cont.)*

In the box below, draw a picture of what your group's ecosystem might look like.

Complete these sentences.

An ecosystem is _____

_____

_____.

Ecology is the study of _____

_____

_____.

Little Sprout

Question

What is a producer?

Setting the Stage

- Have students brainstorm what the word *producer* might mean. Ask them if they have ever heard the word used before and in what way. Make a class list of all the ideas and uses.
- Show students a variety of plants. Using pictures, actual plants, or a combination of both, have students compare the plants and list what they have in common.
- Discuss with students what plants need in order to grow.

Materials Needed for Each Group

- alfalfa or bean sprout seeds (can be found at health food stores)
- glass or jar
- cheesecloth or fine netting
- rubber band
- water
- data-capture sheet (page 15), one per student

Procedure

1. Have students soak some seeds in water the night before the activity.
2. Then have students secure the cheesecloth or netting over the top of their jars with rubber bands so that it droops slightly in the center.
3. Ask the class to compare the seeds that have been soaked overnight with the seeds that are dry. Discuss what is happening to the seeds.
4. Allow students to place a teaspoon (13 g) of seeds on top of their cheesecloth or netting. Have them carefully rinse the seeds with a small amount of water, leaving the rinse water in the bottom of the jar.
5. Have students put the seeds in a dark place overnight and complete Part I of their data-capture sheet.
6. Everyday, students should carefully rinse the seeds with water, keeping them in a dark place until the sprouts have reached 1"-2" (2.5-5 cm). Students can record their observations on their data-capture sheets by sketching what they observe in the appropriate area.
7. When the sprouts have reached 1"-2" (2.5-5 cm), have students stop rinsing them and put the sprouts in a sunny place. Continue to observe and record the growth of the sprouts on your data-capture sheets for up to ten days.

Extensions

- Have students grow other types of producers.
- Have students plant sprouts in soil and see what happens.

Closure

In their ecology journals, have students describe what a producer is.

Little Sprout *(cont.)*

Fill in the information needed.

Part I:

Predict what will happen to the seeds.

I predict that _____

_____

Draw a picture of what the seeds
look like on top of the glass or jar.

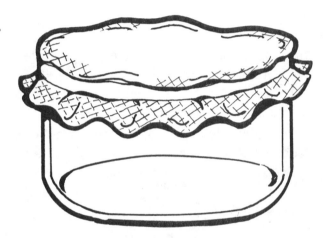

Part II:

Observe your seeds daily and sketch what you see. Remember to use color.

Day 2	Day 3	Day 4	Day 5

Day 6	Day 7	Day 8	Day 9	Day 10

Producer Bingo

Question

What are the producers in our school or neighborhood?

Setting the Stage

- Brainstorm producers with the class, listing them on the chalkboard.
- Discuss with students the different characteristics of producers.

Materials Needed for Each Individual

- clipboard or something to write on
- pencil
- data-capture sheet (page 17)

Procedure

1. Explain to students that they are going to take a walk to look for producers. When they find a producer that has a characteristic on their data-capture sheet, they can draw a circle around that characteristic. Tell your class that the goal of bingo is to circle five boxes in a vertical, horizontal, or diagonal row.
2. Take students for a walk around the school or neighborhood. Encourage students not only to look, but also to touch, smell, and listen. Tell students not to pick anything and to be quiet so they do not disturb the ecosystem.
3. Remind students to circle the producer characteristics that they observe during the walk.
4. If a student finds five characteristics in a row, have him/her quietly say "Producer Bingo."

Extensions

- Have students create original data-capture sheets for each other.
- Have students make up a data-capture sheet for a local nursery, zoo, or even grocery store.

Closure

- After returning to the class, have students share what they observed. Ask the class if anyone observed anything different or something not on the data-capture sheet.
- Discuss the variety of producers and their characteristics found locally.
- Ask students to play Producer Bingo at home and see how it compares to the school or neighborhood.
- Discuss the role of producers in the neighborhood. They provide food, oxygen, shade, a place to play, homes for animals, etc..

Producer Bingo *(cont.)*

I took a walk around my _____.

I observed producers, and this is what I found.

Circle the characteristics that you observed.

PRODUCER BINGO

smooth bark	pointed leaves	fruit	smells good	small flowers
large flowers	in the sun	fuzzy leaves	narrow leaves	in the shade
thin branches	roots	**FREE SPACE**	seeds	flexible branches
leaf clusters	stiff branches	rounded leaves	green	rough bark
thorns	near water	flower clusters	thick branches	vegetables

How Does Your Garden Grow?

Question

What are the variables needed to make a producer grow?

Setting the Stage

- Discuss with students what producers need to grow.
- List for your class the variables associated with plant growth.

Materials Needed for Each Group

- bean seeds
- tape for labeling
- potting soil
- sand
- mulch
- measuring cups
- window sill
- plastic bags
- warm spot
- worms
- ruler
- containers
- clay
- stones
- water
- artificial light
- boxes
- refrigerator
- fertilizer
- data-capture sheets (pages 20-21), one per student

Procedure

1. Show students a bean seed. Is it a producer? What might it need to grow? Review the list of variables associated with plant growth.
2. Assign each group of students a specific variable and ask them to discuss a plan for testing the importance of their variable. (A list of variables with suggested testing methods is on page 19.)
3. Have each group propose a way of testing their variable (page 20).
4. Allow the students to present their proposals to the class. Encourage the class to provide positive comments and suggestions.
5. Have students gather needed materials, set up, and begin their experiences.
6. Students should check for germination and growth on a daily basis. Once growth begins, students should record the growth and their observations on their data-capture sheets (page 21).

Extensions

- Have students predict which will grow the fastest and the tallest. Explain predictions.
- Have students collect pictures from magazines of producers and make a collage of producers.
- Allow students to research any producer of their choice and write a brief report on its growing condition requirements and geographical area in which it is found. Students can represent the information visually by drawing a poster that accompanies their report.
- Have students grow other types of plants from bulbs, runners, etc.

Closure

Have students share the results of their experiences with the class. Then in their ecology journals, have students graph the growth of their bean seeds and make a list of requirements for the beans to grow.

How Does Your Garden Grow? *(cont.)*

Variables and Suggested Testing Methods

Light

Plant seeds in three containers. Place one container in a window sill, another in a box or closet, and a third under a plant light for 24 hours of light.

Temperature

Plant seeds in three containers. Place one container by a heater, another in a freezer or refrigerator, and a third in a room temperature environment.

Gases

Plant seeds in two containers. Cover one container with a plastic bag limiting carbon dioxide/oxygen, but leave the other container uncovered.

Soil

Plant some seeds in potting soil and the same number of seeds in a container with a wet paper towel, but no soil.

Soil Organisms

Plant seeds in organic soil from a garden or forest and the same number of seeds in soil that has been baked to kill all organisms.

Water

Plant the seeds in four separate containers. Give each container a different amount of water: no water, 2-3 tsp (10-15 mL) of water every other day, 1/4 cup (60 mL) of water every other day, and 1/2 cup (125 mL) of water every other day.

Fertilizer

Plant seeds in two containers. Fertilize the soil in one container but not the other.

Worms

Plant seeds in two containers. Add 2-3 earthworms to one container and no earthworms to the other container.

How Does Your Garden Grow? *(cont.)*

Discuss how you plan to test the importance of your variable. Complete this form, explaining how you plan to do your experiment.

Ecologists: _____

The variable we are testing is _____.

Materials Needed:

Procedure:

How Does Your Garden Grow? *(cont.)*

Ecologists: _____

Our variable is _____.

The seeds were planted on_____.

Visible growth began _____days later.

Growth Chart			
	Bean 1	Bean 2	Bean 3
Day Measurement Observation			
Day Measurement Observation			
Day Measurement Observation			
Day Measurement Observation			
Day Measurement Observation			

For the Birds

Question

What is a *consumer?*

Setting the Stage

- Develop a list of ways students have heard the words *consume* and *consumer* used.
- Explain to students that they are going to pretend to be birds. Ask them what birds eat.

Materials Needed for Each Group

- 200 colored candy worms or 1" x 3" (2.54 cm x 7.5 cm) strips of colored paper
- a grassy area
- large graph paper
- colored markers that match the colors of the candy worms/paper
- roll of masking tape

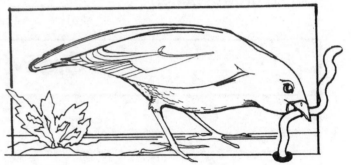

Procedure

1. Prior to bringing the class outdoors, sprinkle the "worms" all around the grassy area. (This activity can be done in a classroom or multi-purpose room as well.)
2. Tell students they need to find their favorite food...worms! To simulate bird's beaks, tape each child's fingers together. (Tape four fingers of the child's dominant hand together, leaving the thumb free.)
3. Demonstrate to students how they are to pick up the worms. They should only use their "beaks," closing taped fingers to thumb. Other hands must be in pockets or behind the students' backs.
4. Take your class outdoors and give them 30 seconds to gather their worms. Stop and record on the graph the exact number of worms that have been collected by color.
5. Have students continue the game for 2-3 more rounds, collecting as many of the remaining worms as they can. Graph the results after each round.
6. Untape the student's hands. Collect the tape. Gather the class in a circle to discuss the results of their being consumers. Which worms were easiest and which the hardest to find? What was difficult about using their beaks?

Extensions

- Take your class to visit a nature center and go on a bird walk with a naturalist. Observe birds consuming.
- Have students set up a worm farm. Get a large jar and fill it with a rich soil. Place worms in the jar. Sprinkle coffee grounds on the top of the soil for the worms to eat. Have the students observe the worms.

Closure

Review the word *consumer* with students. Then in their ecology journals, have students brainstorm a list of bird consumers and the foods they eat.

22

Decompose in Peace

Question

What is a *decomposer?*

Setting the Stage

- Show students a log. Place the log in a magic box, say the magic words, and pull out a rotting log. Place the rotting log back in the box, say the magic words, and pull out pieces of the rotting log. Place the rotting pieces of log back in the box, say the magic words, and pull out a handful of sawdust. Finally, place the sawdust back in the box, say the magic words, and pull out a handful of soil. Discuss with students what has just taken place and tell them how long this process would really take.

- Introduce to your students the terms, *decomposition, decay,* and *rot.* Encourage students to use these new words in sentences that demonstrate their understanding of the words.

Materials Needed for Each Group

- trowel or large spoon for digging
- bucket for the soil
- place to collect soil
- hand lenses or magnifying glasses
- newspaper
- data-capture sheet (page 24), one per student

Procedure

1. Take your class to an area where each group can dig up 2-3 cups (500-750 g) of soil. If that is not possible, have students bring in soil from home or bring it in yourself. Note: Do not buy potting soil; it must be "alive."

2. Once the soil is collected, bring it into the classroom and pour it onto newspaper. Allow students to sort through it looking for animals. They may use hand lenses or magnifying glasses to get a better look.

3. Have students draw pictures of what they see on their data-capture sheets and then identify the animals with a field guide or other resource.

4. Discuss with your class the roles of the decomposers found in the collected soil.

Extension

Have students make a mini-composter using the soil they collected.

Closure

In their ecology journals, have students write about the importance of decomposers in different ecosystems. They may also wish to add drawings.

Decompose in Peace *(cont.)*

Use the space below to draw pictures of the animals you saw in the soil.

24

Goldfish Habitat

Question

What is important to have in a *habitat?*

Setting the Stage

- Tell students to imagine they are going to establish a new community. Have each student list the ten most important things they will need to have in their community. Share the lists of important items. Now, have students pick the three things they could absolutely not do without.

- Introduce to students the term *habitat.*

Materials Needed for Each Group

- goldfish
- fish bowl/aquarium
- sand, rocks, and/or gravel
- aquatic plants and/or filter
- thermometer
- fish food
- observation journal (construction paper folded in half with several data-capture sheets, page 26, stapled inside)

Procedure

1. Announce to the class that they are going to get some goldfish. Brainstorm a list of things that will be needed to make a goldfish habitat.

2. Review with students the things the fish must have to live. Does the list include all of these needs?

3. Obtain the materials needed and set up the fish bowl/aquarium in your classroom.

4. Establish a care schedule for the goldfish. Every day have two students observe the habitat conditions of the fish bowl/aquarium and record their observations in their observation journal. Continue this at least until everyone has had a turn.

5. Share the data with the class once a week and ask students to make suggestions about how to care for the goldfish.

Extensions

- Have students set up habitats for other classroom pets.

- Have a pet store employee visit and explain the different habitat requirements of different fish: temperature, water type, space, food requirements, etc..

- Have students research fish adaptations: gills, fins, scales, etc..

Closure

In their ecology journal, have students define the word *habitat.*

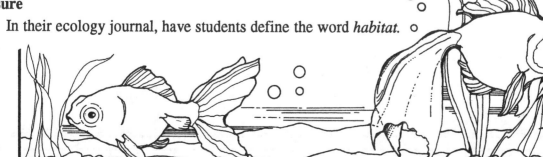

Goldfish Habitat *(cont.)*

Date _____

Temperature of water_____

Temperature of classroom air _____

Number of times fish breathes in one minute (Count the number of times the operculum—gill flap—opens and shuts.) _____

If there are live plants, how do they look?
    ❑ healthy   ❑ unhealthy

How does the water look?
    ❑ clear   ❑ slightly cloudy   ❑ very cloudy

How does the bottom of the tank look?
    ❑ clean   ❑ slightly dirty   ❑ very dirty

How does the glass look?
    ❑ clear   ❑ some algae   ❑ much algae

Where did the fish feed?
    ❑ on the surface   ❑ in the middle   ❑ on the bottom

How much food was left over?
    ❑ none   ❑ little   ❑ much

Water, Water, Everywhere

Question

How much usable water is a part of each ecosystem?

Setting the Stage

- Discuss with students the ways in which we use water and list them.
- Have class brainstorm how other animals use water.

Materials Needed for Class

- six 1 gallon (4 L) jugs filled with water
- measuring cup
- six clear containers at least 16 oz. (500 mL)
- data-capture sheet (page 28), one per student
- one 1/2 gallon (2 L) jug half-filled with water
- measuring spoons
- masking tape

Procedure

1. Tell your class that the water in the jugs represents all the water in the world.
2. Using a world map, have students locate and develop a list of places that water is found naturally: oceans, ice/glaciers, groundwater, freshwater, inland seas/salt lakes, atmosphere, and rivers. Using masking tape, label one container for each category of water except oceans.
3. Divide your class into small groups. Have the groups predict how much of the water will be in each. Group members should fill out their data-capture sheets on their own first, then as a group.
4. Have students share their predictions.
5. Using the water in the jugs, have students pour the indicated amounts into each labeled container.

    ice/glaciers—2 cups (500 mL)

    groundwater—8 tbsp (120 mL)

    freshwater lakes—1 tsp (5 mL)

    inland seas/salt lakes—1 tsp (5 mL)

    atmosphere—1/4 tsp (1.25 mL)

    rivers —1/16 tsp (.26 mL)

6. Tell students that the water in each container represents the world's water supply in that category. The water remaining in the jugs, about 97 cups (24 L) represents the water in the oceans.

Extensions

- Ask students what bodies of water they have heard about. Help students locate them on a world map.
- Have students identify the bodies of water in their community.
- Have students brainstorm ways to conserve water.

Closure

Discuss with your class what the model teaches about the amount of fresh water that is available for human use and other consumers. Have students complete their data-capture sheets and add them to their ecology journals.

Water, Water, Everywhere *(cont.)*

If you have 100 cups (25 L) of water in the world, how much would be in each of these categories? Be sure your estimates total 100 cups (25 L).

Category	Your Estimate	Group Estimate	Actual
oceans			
ice/glaciers			
freshwater			
inland seas/ salt lakes			
groundwater			
atmosphere			
rivers			

28

Follow That Water

Question

How is water recycled in an ecosystem?

Setting the Stage

- Ask students a "water puzzler," such as: *How could the water that I drank this morning be the same water that the dinosaurs walked in?* or, *How could the water I took a shower in be the same water that Christopher Columbus took a shower in?'*
- Survey the class for their feelings about this. Did they think it was true or false? How could they prove it?

Materials Needed for Each Group

- paper cups
- construction paper
- yarn
- water
- markers
- data-capture sheet (page 31), one per student

Procedure

1. Make a set of signs using construction paper, markers, and yarn to hang around student's necks. The signs should include these words (for younger students draw a picture with the word): lake, ocean, atmosphere, clouds, rain, snow, groundwater, river, mountain, well, house, tree, and sun.
2. Ask students wearing the signs to stand in the front of the class. As they come forward, give each an empty cup. Describe how the students are going to be a part of a water model and that by the end of the activity they will be able to answer the water puzzler that started the lesson.

Follow That Water *(cont.)*

Procedure *(cont.)*

3. Begin by filling the lake's and ocean's cups with water. Have them consider whether their water always stays there. Have them describe how some of their water might be moved to another place. Look at the other signs for hints. Ask them to pour some of their water into the atmosphere's cup, thanks to the sun (evaporation).

4. Next, ask the atmosphere to think about where its water might end up, and then to transfer that water to the clouds.

5. Ask the clouds to repeat the process and transfer some of their water into snow and rain.

6. Repeat the process with snow and rain giving a little water to the tree, mountain, and groundwater. The mountain might have the snow melt and run into a river. The groundwater might give some water to the well. The well would then pass some water to the house, which would then pass it back to the lake, ocean, or river. Continue the process until it starts over again.

7. At this point, all should have had some water in their cups at some time. Once the class has finished the demonstration, discuss what they did. Was more water added? Was water taken away (excluding water that was spilled)? Explain how the model is like our real water cycle and that the water we had to start with is the water we have now and will have in the future.

8. Refer to the water puzzler and ask it again. Now what do the students think?

Extensions

- Have students set up glasses of water around the room and measure the changes in water level over time to record evaporation.
- Have students put a plastic bag over a plant to see if any water transpires.
- Boil a kettle of water and then put a glass or mirror in the steam. Ask students how condensation is like a cloud.
- Discuss with students humidity in the air. Have students measure it or look up the humidity reading in the newspaper.

Closure

In their ecology journals, have students define the following terms: *evaporation, condensation, precipitation*, and *run-off*.

Follow That Water *(cont.)*

Draw the water cycle below. Label the water cycle with the key words in the box. Draw arrows to show how the water moves through the cycle.

evaporation	condensation	precipitation	run-off

An Apple a Day

Question
Where do you find water in a food chain?

Setting the Stage
- Create a food chain that ends with a person: For example, sun - apple tree (apple) - person. Discuss with students where the water is in the food chain.
- Ask students if the apple has water in it. Do we get water from the apple? Discuss with students ways to prove that an apple has water in it.

Materials Needed for Each Group
- apples, one per group
- knife
- scale
- weights
- thread
- needle
- data-capture sheet (page 33), one per student

Procedure
1. Give each group an apple to weigh. Have them record the weight on their data-capture sheets.
2. Help students slice their apples into 7-8 thin slices.
3. Have students weigh their apples again and record on their data-capture sheets. They should weigh the same as they did before they were sliced.
4. Have students thread the apple slices. Save any pieces that fall off in a plastic bag. Hang the apple pieces up in a warm dry place.
5. After one week, have students weigh the apples again and record the weight on their data-capture sheet. Discuss the changes that have happened.
6. Have students continue the drying process until the apples are completely dry.

Extension
Have students repeat the process with other fruits. Which fruits contain the most water?

Closure
Compare the weights recorded on the data-capture sheet. Discuss with the class what happened. What caused the decrease in weight? What is no longer there? Review how water evaporates and that the water is now a part of the atmosphere. Discuss how water has become a part of the food chain along with energy from the sun.

An Apple a Day *(cont.)*

Weight of apple: _____

Weight of apple after sliced: _____

Weight of apple after one week   _____

Observations: _____

Weight of apple after two weeks   _____

Observations: _____

Weight of apple after three weeks   _____

Observations: _____

Weight of apple at end of experiment   _____

Observations: _____

Calculate the weight change.

Weight of the apple in the beginning: _____

Weight of the apple at the end: _____

Weight change: _____

How much water was lost?   _____

Where did this water go? _____

_____

Just the Facts

In an ecosystem all the organisms work together just like all the members of your community work together. Now think about taking away a few of the jobs or businesses in your community. What would happen to your community if the postal delivery people were taken away? Or if there were no people to pick up your garbage? Or if there were no grocery stores? Everyone in your community is dependent on somebody else. Make a list of all the people in the community you are dependent upon.

Ecosystems involve living and nonliving components. Remember what some of those components are? In order to see how the members of an ecosystem are interdependent, you will need to understand a few new words.

- **POPULATION**—A population is the number of organisms in a specified area. What is the population of your school?

- **CARRYING CAPACITY**—The number of organisms an environment can support is its carrying capacity. What is the carrying capacity of your school? What factors determine how many students can attend your school?

- **PREDATOR**—Any animal that hunts and eats other animals is called a predator. Make a list of predators.

- **PREY**—Any animal that is hunted and eaten by other animals is called prey. The relationship between a predator and prey is very important in ecology. Make a list of animals which are often prey.

- **HABITAT**—The environment in which a plant or animal can naturally be found is its habitat.

- **NICHE**—The role an organism plays is an ecosystem is its niche. Think about any jobs you have at home. Your family depends on you to do those jobs. Your niche is your job in your home, your habitat.

It is also important to know that there are four types of **CONSUMERS.**

- **HERBIVORES**—Animals that eat only plants.

- **CARNIVORES**—Animals that eat only other animals.

- **OMNIVORES**—Animals that eat both plants and animals.

- **SCAVENGERS**—Animals that do not kill their own food, but eat what is left of a dead plant or animal.

Which type of consumer are you?

Wait Your Turn

Question

What are some examples of food chains in different ecosystems?

Setting the Stage

- Discuss with your students the term *food chain*.
- Have five student volunteers help model a forest food chain. The students can hold up signs or pictures that can be easily identified by their classmates. For example: sun-oak tree-squirrel-bobcat-fungi.
- Have your students identify producers, consumers, and decomposers.

Materials Needed for Each Group

- description of food chain
- mural paper
- colored markers or crayons
- data-capture sheet (page 36), one per student
- pictures of animals, plants, and habitats of different ecosystems: arctic tundra, desert, forest, pond, ocean, etc. (These can be found in magazines, books, and encyclopedias.)

Procedure

1. Assign students a food chain for a specific ecosystem.
2. Have students use a combination of pictures you provide and their own drawings to create their assigned food chain on the mural paper.
3. Once complete, have students share their food chains with other groups.
4. Discuss with the class the ways in which they help and hurt ecosystems. How does this affect food chains?
5. After the discussion, have students return to their groups and make their own lists of things that would help and hurt their ecosystems (record on data-capture sheet). Then, share the lists with their group members and make a master list on their murals.

Extensions

- Have students research

  1) specific ecosystems (oceans, rain forests, wetlands, etc.) that are being affected by humans and 2) the food chains that identify the species living within them.

- With your class, adopt an ecosystem in your area that you and your class can help to protect.

Closure

In their ecology journals, have students write a story about their food chains and ecosystems.

Wait Your Turn *(cont.)*

Think of ways to help your ecosystem or harm your ecosystem. List your ideas below.

Our ecosystem is_____.

	Ways to Help		**Ways to Hurt**
1.	_____	1.	_____
2.	_____	2.	_____
3.	_____	3.	_____
4.	_____	4.	_____
5.	_____	5.	_____
6.	_____	6.	_____
7.	_____	7.	_____
8.	_____	8.	_____
9.	_____	9.	_____
10.	_____	10.	_____

Consume the Consumer

Question

How are different consumers adapted to survive?

Setting the Stage

- Discuss with students the different levels of consumers (predator/prey relationships).
- Have the class list a variety of animals on the board, list each animal's adaptation for survival, and then discuss those adaptations.

Materials Needed for Class

- three construction paper squares 2" x 2" (5 cm x 5 cm) per student
- bandannas to denote predators
- 3-5 large pieces of rope or hula hoops
- playing field or gym
- data-capture sheet (page 38), one per student

Procedure

1. Divide students into predators (wolves) and prey (deer), one wolf for every ten deer.
2. Tell your students they are going to participate in a predator/prey simulation using adaptations.
3. When you arrive at the playing area, tell the deer that one end is their permanent food source, the other end is their shelter, and the area in the middle is open territory, with 3-5 temporary shelters (pieces of rope or hula hoops).
4. The wolves may only use the open territory, trying to capture the deer for food by tagging them. Once a deer has been tagged, it must sit down on the sidelines and wait for the next round. Each wolf must tag two deer in order to survive through the simulation.
5. In order for the deer to get food, it must go from its shelter to the food source, pick up one food piece, (paper square), and return to its shelter. The deer must do this three times in order to survive.
6. When the deer try to collect their food, they have several options in avoiding the wolves: to run away, to avoid being seen by not moving, or to hide in a temporary shelter.
7. Each round should last about five minutes. Play several rounds so students can be both predator and prey.
8. At the end of the simulation, have students complete the data-capture sheets and discuss their answers in class.

Extensions

- Have students participate in the same simulation, but this time incorporate limiting factors.
- Have students pick animals of their choice, research their survival adaptations, and report to the class.

Closure

In their ecology journals, have students create their own animals and adaptations.

Consume the Consumers *(cont.)*

Answer the following questions.

1. What was the easiest way for you to escape from the wolf?

   _____

   _____

2. What was the most effective way for you to escape from the wolf?

   _____

   _____

3. What was the best way for you to catch the deer?

   _____

   _____

4. What did you do when a deer you were chasing "froze"?

   _____

   _____

5. How are adaptations important to both predator and prey?

   _____

   _____

6. Write a summary of the importance of predator/prey relationships?

   _____

   _____

   _____

All in a Day's Work

Question

How are predator and prey animals consumers?

Setting the Stage

- Define *predator* and *prey*.
- Survey the class for examples of predator/prey relationships.
- Come up with a class definition of *population*.

Materials Needed for Class

- whistle
- 30 strips of cloth, 1'-2' (30 cm-60 cm) long
- four cones to mark boundaries of playing field
- copy of rules on poster board
- three colored markers
- data-capture sheet (page 41), one per student

Procedure

1. Explain the rules to the class. (See page 40.)
2. Outline the playing field.
3. Explain how the populations will be recorded on the graph. Have three students volunteer to be recorders, one for each population.
4. Divide the class into three groups according to the following percentages: 65% grass, 25% rabbits, 10% foxes.
5. Play the game for four or five rounds or until the population balance is such that there is not enough food for one population to survive.
6. Discuss with students the outcome of the game by reflecting on the population numbers and cycles in the graph. Analyze the graph. Ask students how the population of one species is affected by that of another.

Extensions

- Have students play the game again but add variables, such as a hunter that hunts the fox or an herbicide sprayed on the producers to kill weeds but which also kills some grass. Record the results on a new graph. Discuss the changes.
- Have students research a population of animals that is threatened or endangered. Highlight the reasons the population is declining. Discuss the other species that might be impacted by the change in population size of the research species.

Closure

Review with the class the population cycles of the grass, rabbits, and foxes. In their ecology journals, have students describe the stages of population change.

All in a Day's Work *(cont.)*

Predator - Prey Game

The goal of the game is for the rabbits to get a piece of grass back to their hutch before the end of the day and for the fox to catch a rabbit before the end of the day.

Set-up

The field is set up in a rectangle. A 40' x 60' (12 m x 18 m) field is recommended. At one end of the field is the grass. The rabbits live at the other end of the field. The middle of the field is the foxes' territory.

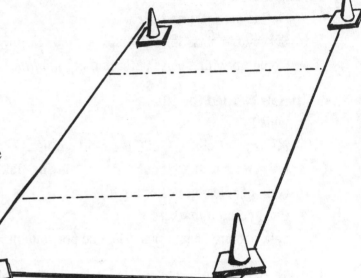

The game will be played in a series of "days." The day begins with a whistle being blown and stops with two whistles. Everyone must stop and freeze at the end of the day so that the recorders can count and record their results on the graph (page 41).

Rules

1. A rabbit must run down to the grass field and grab one "grass" and run hand-in-hand with that grass back to the hutch before the end of the day.

2. The grass may not leave the grass field unless they are holding hands with a rabbit.

3. All rabbits must wear a tail (strip of cloth) tucked into their pants or skirt. The tail must be visible and easily removed with a slight tug.

4. A fox must catch one, and only one, rabbit by the end of the day. A rabbit is caught when the fox has the rabbit's tail.

5. A fox may not catch rabbits in their shelter or on the grass field. (These are safety zones for rabbits and grass).

6. If a fox catches a rabbit, they are to step to the side of the field and wait for the end of the day. The next round, the rabbit becomes a fox, and the fox remains a fox.

7. If a fox does not catch a rabbit, the fox dies and goes to the grass field the next day.

8. If the fox catches a rabbit that is holding hands with a grass, the rabbit becomes a fox the next round, but the grass returns to the grass field.

9. If the rabbit and the grass both get back to the hutch before the end of the day, the rabbit stays a rabbit the next round and the grass becomes a rabbit.

10. If the rabbit does not get a piece of grass, the rabbit dies and goes to the grass field for the next day.

11. Grass, rabbits, and foxes must report to their appropriate spots at the end of the day so the recorders can mark the population size on the graph.

All in a Day's Work *(cont.)*

☐ fox   ☐ rabbit   ☐ grass

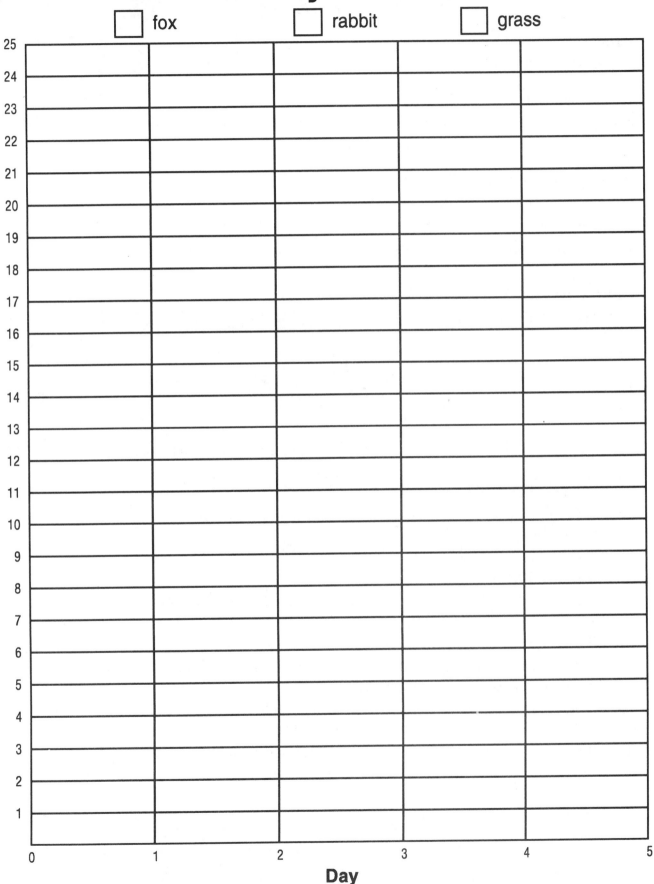

Day

Worm Works

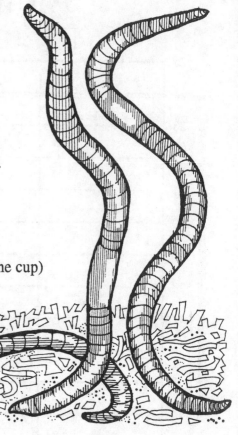

Question

What do decomposers do?

Setting the Stage

- Review what decomposers are.
- Have the class brainstorm a list of different types of decomposers.

Materials Needed for Each Student

- one 16 oz. (500 mL) clear plastic cup
- newspaper
- 2-3 handfuls of leaves or shredded newspaper (should fill 2/3 of the cup)
- spray bottle filled with water (This may be shared.)
- 2-3 earthworms
- 3 tablespoons (45 g) of soil
- two slices of fruit or vegetable
- data-capture sheet (page 43)

Procedure

1. Cover the work area with newspaper.
2. Have students put the leaves or shredded newspaper on the newspaper and moisten them with the spray bottle.
3. Students should mix the soil with the leaves or newspaper.
4. Have students add half their mixture to their cups. They need to put their fruit or vegetable slices in the cup so that they can see them.
5. Give each student 2-3 earthworms to put in their cups.
6. Put remaining mixture in the cups. Do not pack the mixture down.
7. Have students observe the activity of the worms for two weeks, recording observations on the data-capture sheet.

Extensions

- Research other decomposers and make a display of them.
- Make a school composter to recycle lunch waste.

Closure

- Discuss what happened with the class. What happened to the fruit or vegetable slices? What did the earthworms do?
- Discuss the niche of decomposers in an ecosystem.

Worm Works *(cont.)*

This is what my worm habitat looks like. Worms live here.

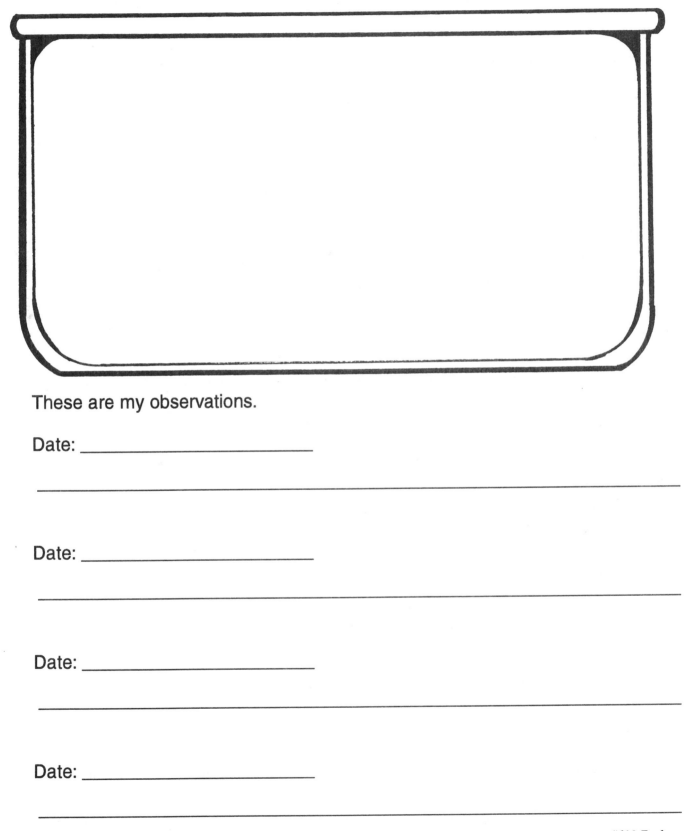

These are my observations.

Date: _____

_____

Date: _____

_____

Date: _____

_____

Date: _____

_____

You Are What You Eat

Question

What are *herbivores, carnivores,* and *omnivores?*

Setting the Stage

In this activity students are going to differentiate between an herbivore, carnivore, and omnivore. It is important that you are clear on the difference.

* **Herbivore**—only eats plants
* **Carnivore**—only eats meat
* **Omnivore**—eats meat and plants

Materials Needed for Each Pair

- scissors
- glue
- large paper
- animal cards (page 45)
- data-capture sheet (page 46), one per student

Procedure

1. Have students cut out all the animal cards (page 45).
2. Ask the students to put all the animals into groups by what they eat. They must be able to explain why every animal is in that group. For example, they may group five animals together because they all eat plants.
3. When students have finished, groups can walk around the classroom comparing and contrasting different classification systems. A challenge can be presented to see if different groups can figure out how each group organized their classification systems.
4. After students have shared their systems, introduce the terms: herbivore—plant eater, carnivore—meat eater, omnivore—plant and animal eater. Ask the students to regroup their animals into these three categories.
5. After students have finished this activity, have them research an animal of their choice using page 46.

Extensions

- Take your class on a field trip to a natural history museum or zoo and identify each animal as a herbivore, carnivore, or omnivore.
- Invite a biologist to speak to your class about animal adaptations.
- Have students make three bulletin boards that are collages of the three different types of animals: herbivores, carnivores, omnivores. Use student art work, magazine and calendar pictures, etc.

Closure

In their ecology journals, have students write *herbivore, carnivore*, and *omnivore* and brainstorm a list of animals for each category.

You Are What You Eat (cont.)

fox	wolf	deer	rabbit	human
raccoon	bear	mouse	cricket	snake
snail	clam	dolphin	butterfly	owl
Canada goose	dog	cat	goldfish	painted turtle
elk	bobcat	opossum	porcupine	honeybee
coyote	mink	dove	cardinal	hawk

You Are What You Eat *(cont.)*

Use books, magazines, encyclopedias, and computer resources to find the answers to these questions.

Name of animal being researched: _____

Is it an herbivore, carnivore, or omnivore?_____

What is its typical diet? What is its favorite food? _____

_____

_____

How does it get its food? What adaptations does it have for gathering or catching its food?

_____

_____

_____

_____

What type of habitat does your animal live in?

_____

_____

List three interesting facts about your animal.

1. _____

2. _____

3. _____

Scavenger Search

Question

What is a scavenger?

Setting the Stage

- Have students imagine that they are in a wilderness area. As they walk through the area, they come across a partially eaten rabbit. Ask them what animal might have eaten it, why an animal would not finish eating its prey, and what would happen to the rabbit remains.

- Show students a picture of a vulture. Discuss with students that vultures like to eat dead animal remains and really help to clean up the "leftovers."

Materials Needed for the Class

- 100 pennies/counters
- data-capture sheet (page 48), one per student

Procedure

In this game, the students will be scavengers.

Their goal is to collect as many animal remains (pennies/counters) as possible.

1. In your classroom, hide 100 pennies/counters.

2. Split the class into three groups.

3. The first group of students will be the first vultures to arrive in the "woodland ecosystem," your classroom. They are to search for animal remains. Give them 30-60 seconds to search, and then they should return to their seats.

4. Now it is the second group's turn. They should be given the same amount of time as the first group.

5. Finally, allow the third group to do their search.

6. Fill in the data-capture sheet, as a class or individually, so that it reflects the number of pennies/counters found as each group entered the woods.

7. Discuss with students what happened as the different groups came searching. Which scavengers had the easiest time? How is the decreasing number of pennies/counters like the decreasing amount of available animal remains in an ecosystem? Would an ecosystem run out of animal remains like your classroom ecosystem did? Why not? Discuss with students how there is a constant source of animal remains for scavengers. What sources of animal remains might supply the scavengers with food other than animals that had been eaten by predators? (road kills, animals that died from sickness or starvation, etc.)

Extensions

- Take the students for a walk in a park or nature area. Have them observe scavengers at work.

- Have them research different types of birds that are scavengers.

Closure

In their ecology journals, have students explain what a scavenger is and what it is like to be one.

Scavenger Search *(cont.)*

Record the number of animal remains (pennies/counters) recovered.

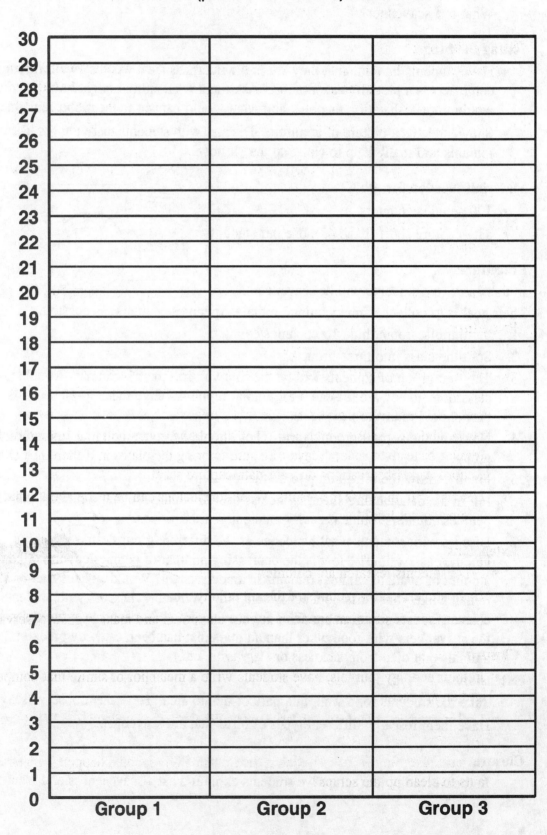

48

Ant Picnic

Question

What role do scavengers play in a food chain?

Setting the Stage

- Have the class imagine that they just had a picnic. Are there leftovers? Are there parts that are thrown out? Are there any food pieces that get spilled or dropped on the ground? What happens to those parts? Have they ever seen any animals around their picnics that like to eat those scraps?

- Point out to students that food chains are often like a picnic. There are places in the food chain where parts do not get eaten, pieces get left behind, etc. Fortunately, there are animals that like to clean up those pieces, and they are called scavengers. Brainstorm a list of animals that the students have seen as scavengers.

Materials Needed for Each Group

- paper plate
- honey
- food scraps
- coffee grounds
- markers
- data-capture sheet (page 50), one per student

Procedure

1. Split the class into small groups.
2. Using a marker, have each group divide their paper plate into four sections.
3. On each section, have students put a small amount of honey, coffee grounds, or food scraps.
4. Have students set the plates outside in an area where ants have been seen.
5. Have students predict which section of the plate the ants will like best. Check the plates on a regular basis over several days. (Be sure to bring the plates in if there is a chance of rain.) Record daily observations on your data-capture sheet.
6. Discuss with the class the results. What conclusions can be made about what types of food ants like or do not like?

Extensions

- Have students research ant colonies.
- Have students draw pictures of the ant colony.
- Have students set up an ant farm in your classroom and make regular observations.

Closure

- In their ecology journals, have students write a metaphor or simile that compares a family picnic and an ant picnic.
- Use magnifying glasses to observe ants. What are they collecting? What type of habitat do the ants like? How is their habitat like the ant picnic?
- Discuss the role of scavengers in a food chain. What would happen if there were no animals like ants to clean up the scraps?

Ant Picnic *(cont.)*

Fill in the picture and label each section.

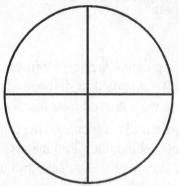

Observe the picnic daily. Record any changes that occur. Draw in changes and write in observations.

Day 1

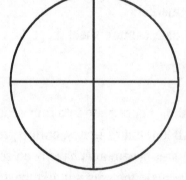

_____

_____

_____

_____

Day 2

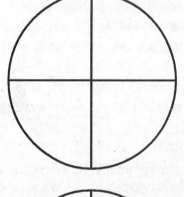

_____

_____

_____

_____

Day 3

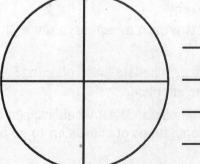

_____

_____

_____

_____

Producer-Consumer Census

Question

Which is there more of in an ecosystem, producers or consumers?

Setting the Stage

- Review *producer, consumer*, and *population* with students.
- As a class write out a six-part food chain. Identify the producer, consumers, and scavengers/decomposers.
- Show students an example to introduce the terms *primary consumer, secondary consumer, top consumer.*

    Food Chain Example: sun-algae-oyster-seastar-crab-fish-osprey

    Algae is the producer.

    Oyster is the primary consumer because it eats a producer.

    Seastar, crab, and fish are secondary consumers because they eat other consumers.

    Osprey is the top consumer because it is not eaten by anything else.

Materials Needed for Each Individual

data-capture sheets (pages 52-53)

Procedure

1. Take your students for a walk around your school, community, or local park.
2. On their data-capture sheets (page 52), the students are to keep a tally of what they see. They are merely to count the number of producers and consumers, not to identify the species.
3. The students should be timed at three observation points. They are to stand in one spot during the timed period, and pick a different spot for each of the three timed sections. A separate tally should be made for each observation point.
4. Discuss the results of the census with the class. Which was there the most of? What types of consumers did they see? Group these consumers into primary, secondary, and top consumers. Did they see any signs of other consumers? Did they see any scavengers?

Extensions

- Have students repeat census-taking in different locations.
- Discuss with students census-taking for larger populations. What procedures are used? How is the population of the United States taken?
- Show students a census form.

Closure

- Have students calculate totals on their data-capture sheets. Graph the results on page 53.
- In their ecology journals, have students list the factors that cause populations of producers to go up and down and factors that cause populations of consumers to go up and down. Share lists.

Producer-Consumer Census *(cont.)*

At each observation point keep a tally of the producers and consumers you see.

When you finish observing, total your counts from Observation Points 1, 2, and 3.

Producers

Observation Point 1 _____

Observation Point 2 _____

Observation Point 3 _____

Total _____

Observation Point 1	
Producers	
Consumers	

Consumers

Observation Point 1 _____

Observation Point 2 _____

Observation Point 3 _____

Total _____

Observation Point 2	
Producers	
Consumers	

Which has the largest populaton?

_____

_____

Why do you think this is?

_____

_____

_____

Observation Point 3	
Producers	
Consumers	

Producer-Consumer Census *(cont.)*

Name _____

Date _____

Location _____

	30		
	29		
	28		
	27		
	26		
	25		
	24		
	23		
	22		
	21		
	20		
	19		
	18		
	17		
	16		
	15		
	14		
	13		
	12		
	11		
	10		
	9		
	8		
	7		
	6		
	5		
	4		
	3		
	2		
	1		
	0		
		Producers	**Consumers**

Hunter and Hunted

Question

What happens to a population when there is no longer a predator?

Setting the Stage

- Have students make a list of food chains that have a producer, primary consumer, secondary consumer, and top consumer.
- Pick one of those food chains to have the class analyze. What might happen to the population of secondary consumers if there were no top consumers? How would this impact the rest of the food chain on the short term and long term?

Materials Needed for Each Individual

- graph paper
- population statistics (page 55)
- data-capture sheet (page 56)

Procedure

1. Give each student a piece of graph paper and a population statistics sheet.
2. Have students graph the two populations and then answer the questions about the graphs.
3. Discuss the relationship of the two populations with the class. Do they have any effect on each other? Why?

Extensions

- Take your class to visit a park that has a large population of deer and discuss with the park naturalist the issues faced in monitoring and controlling the deer population.
- Have students research the life cycle of deer.

Closure

In their ecology journals, have students describe the predator-prey relationship.

54

Hunter and Hunted *(cont.)*

Year	Deer Population
	(estimated)
1940	150
1945	180
1950	170
1955	150
1960	180
1965	200
1970	220
1975	220
1980	290
1985	320
1990	360
1995	420

Year	Wolf Population
	(estimated)
1940	25
1945	40
1950	40
1955	30
1960	30
1965	25
1970	25
1975	10
1980	8
1985	8
1990	3
1995	0

Hunter and Hunted (cont.)

1. What happened to the deer population when the wolf population increased between 1940 and 1945? Why do you think this happened?

   _____

2. Between 1960 and 1965 what happened to the deer population? What happened to the wolf population during that same time?

   _____

3. From 1975 to 1995 the deer population increased by how much?

   _____

4. From 1975 to 1995, the wolf population decreased by how much?

   _____

5. What would you have expected to happen to the wolf population from 1975-1995 as the deer population was growing?

   _____

6. What might be some causes for the deer population to increase so rapidly?

   _____

7. What might be some causes for the wolf population to decrease so rapidly?

   _____

8. What might happen if the deer population continues to grow so fast? Is there a limit to the deer population that can live on a certain area of land?

   _____

Producer-Consumer Pyramid

Question

What is a *food pyramid?*

Setting the Stage

- Review the results of the Producer-Consumer Census by looking at the graph. Turn the graph on its side so that the producer line is at the bottom of the paper. Discuss with students that in a food pyramid, the bottom layer of the pyramid is made up of producers.

- Have students predict what might happen with the graph if they separated the consumers into primary, secondary and top consumers?

Materials Needed for Each Individual

data-capture sheet (page 58)

Procedure

1. Write Producer, Primary Consumer, Secondary Consumer, and Top Consumer on the chalkboard.

2. Discuss with students how the class might be split up into these groups by population size. Ask students which group would be largest, and which group would be smallest. Explain to the class that roughly these groups break down as follows:

    Producers: 65%
    Primary Consumers: 20%
    Secondary Consumers: 10%
    Top Consumers: 5%

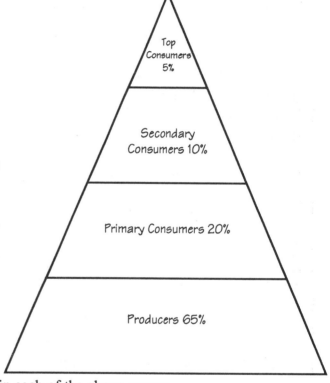

Top Consumers 5%

Secondary Consumers 10%

Primary Consumers 20%

Producers 65%

3. Calculate the number of students that belong in each of the above groups.

4. Have students transfer this information to the graph portion of their data-capture sheet.

Extensions

- Discuss with students factors that could break down the pyramid balance.

- Discuss with students factors that are needed to keep a pyramid stable.

- Visit a zoo with your class and identify each animal as a primary, secondary, or top consumer. Which are there the most of? Which are there the least of? Interview the zookeepers. Where do they get food for the secondary and top consumers?

Closure

In their ecology journals, have students draw pictures of the class food pyramid.

Producer-Consumer Pyramid *(cont.)*

Producers:_____   Secondary Consumers:_____

Primary Consumers: _____   Top Consumers: _____

Complete the bar graph below using a different color for each category.

Top Consumer	
Secondary Consumer	
Primary Consumer	
Producer	

0 1 2 3 4 5 6 7 8 9 10 11 12 13 14 15 16 17 18 19 20 21 22 23 24 25

What's Your Niche?

Question

What is a *niche?*

Setting the Stage

- Bring in a tape of some of your students' favorite music or songs.

- Play the music and ask the students to listen very carefully to all the instruments. List the instruments involved and the different voices. How would the song sound if you took out some of these parts? Discuss how each of the parts has an important role in making the song come together. The singers and instrumentalists all have specific jobs in the band; they each have a special niche. Define *niche.* Help students to define what the different niches are of each person in the band.

Materials Needed for Each Group

- peanut butter
- jelly
- bread
- plastic knife
- paper plate
- napkins
- task cards (page 60)

Procedure

1. Split the class into groups of four. Each group will be a sandwich-making team.

2. Give each person in the group a task card. Each person in the group may do only the task on his/her card.

3. The group is to assemble one peanut butter and jelly sandwich and cut it into four pieces based on the task cards. They may do it in any order they want, but the goal is for everyone in the group to get a quarter of a peanut butter and jelly sandwich. (It is sometimes fun for the students to time themselves and see how long it takes them to make their first sandwich compared to a second sandwich.)

4. When the students are finished, discuss the activity. What were the niches of each person on the sandwich-making team? How were these people dependent on each other? How would the niches be different if you had a more complicated project, such as building a piece of playground equipment or a house?

Extensions

- Have students research the niches of different animals.

- Take a class field trip to a zoo and ask the zookeeper to describe the niches of various animals at the zoo.

Closure

In their ecology journals, have students make a list of all the niches in their school. How are the different people dependent on each other? What does each of these people need to succeed in your school? What are the "habitats" of the different people?

What's Your Niche? *(cont.)*

Master of the Peanut Butter

You may do the following jobs:

- Dip the knife into peanut butter.

- Spread peanut butter on the bread.

Master of the Jelly

You may do the following jobs:

- Dip the knife into jelly.

- Spread jelly on the bread.

Mighty Mover

You may do the following jobs:

- Open peanut butter and jelly jars.

- Open bread bags.

- Cut sandwich into quarters.

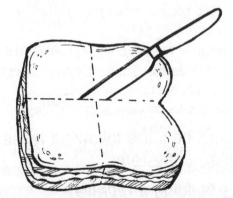

Bread Builder

You may do the following jobs:

- Remove bread from bread bag.

- Place bread on plate.

- Put the two pieces of bread together.

- Pass out a quarter of the sandwich to each team member.

60

Just the Facts

For many years, people have been interacting with their environment. Since all plants, animals, and people share the earth together, it is important to understand how we impact the ecosystems around us. At times, we are helpful to the ecosystem, but at other times we disrupt the balance and can cause damage to the environment, plants, and animals.

How have you interacted with your ecosystem this week? What did you use from the earth? How did you help your ecosystem? How might you have harmed it or upset the delicate balance?

Ecologists and environmentalists are very concerned about monitoring the impact that humans have on ecosystems. We are dependent on many resources from the earth, but we must be sure to maintain these resources for future generations.

Make a list of ways that you know humans have impacted the earth's ecosystems. Think about all the different parts of the world.

Think about all the ways that you have used and impacted the following natural resources.

Water
Plants
Animals
Air
Soil

Think about how the following types of interactions with the environment might impact the ecosystem.

- *Building a highway.*
- *Using water in your home.*
- *Fertilizing your lawn.*
- *Building a new housing development.*
- *Cutting down trees to make lumber and paper.*
- *Fishing and hunting.*
- *Driving a car.*
- *Planting a garden or a tree.*
- *Building a birdhouse or feeding the birds.*

Town Meeting

Question

How do the needs of people impact an ecosystem?

Setting the Stage

- Discuss with your students the term *impact*. Then, relate it to the environment.
- Read your class Dr. Seuss' *The Lorax* or show the movie. Discuss the major themes.

Materials Needed for Each Group

- pen or pencil
- card identifying group (environmentalists, ranchers, shop owners, townspeople, hunters, etc.)
- data-capture sheet (page 63), one per student

Procedure

1. Explain to your class that they will be participating in a town meeting simulation. Then, divide the class into groups of five or six students.
2. Give each group a card that identifies the public interest group they represent.
3. Once each group knows who they represent, you need to decide on a topic for them to debate. Note: It can either be real or made up.
4. Once you decide on a topic, each group must decide if they are for or against that topic. Then, come up with five reasons defending their decision and write them down on their data-capture sheets.
5. Have each group choose one representative to present their position to the class.
6. After all the presentations have been made, the debate may begin. Students may ask any of the representatives questions concerning the topic. If the representative cannot answer the question, it may be directed back to their group. Questioning may continue as long as you like.
7. When the debate is finished, have everyone put their heads on their desks. Take a vote while students are still role-playing. Note: Do not tell the students the outcome yet.
8. The first vote taken was the students role-playing public interest groups. Now have them vote as themselves to see if there is any difference from the first vote. After the second vote has been taken, share the results of both votes with your students.

Extensions

- Take a class field trip to a public hearing and observe what takes place.
- Have students research an environmental topic that is currently being debated and have them share the information with the class.

Closure

In their ecology journals, have students write a letter to a public official about an environmental topic that concerns them.

Town Meeting *(cont.)*

Answer the following questions.

What public interest group do you represent? _____

What topic is being debated? _____

Is your public interest group for or against the topic being debated?

_____

List your five reasons:

1. _____

_____

2. _____

_____

3. _____

_____

4. _____

_____

5. _____

_____

Let's Take a Survey

Question

Which animals and plants do we like the best?

Setting the Stage

- Ask the class what a survey is and why surveys are taken.
- Bring in a selection of survey results from magazines and newspapers. Discuss with students the results of the different surveys.

Materials Needed for Each Individual

- clipboard
- pencil
- graph paper
- data-capture sheets (pages 65 - 66)

   Note to the teacher: The goal of this activity is for students to participate in taking a survey. The results of the survey will be used in a discussion about animal and plant populations, species protection, and endangered species.

Procedure

1. Assign students to groups of four-five. Each student should then survey five people. The results will then be collated and graphed by each group.
2. Students should use their data-capture sheets (page 65) so that they can easily share results.
3. Graphs will need to be constructed on an individual basis according to the results of the survey.
4. Students should then interpret their graphs by answering the questions on page 66.

Extensions

- Have students use computers to set up a spread sheet to do the calculations and organization.
- Discuss with students how results might differ in different areas of the U.S. and different parts of the world. Would the results be different historically? In the future? What things might influence people's choices?

Closure

- Discuss the results of the survey with the class. What might their results tell them about the types of animals and plants people like?
- Discuss with students the connection between the protection of animals that capture people's attention, such as whales and wolves, versus the concern for less popular species. How might they increase the peoples' awareness of lesser known animals?

Let's Take a Survey *(cont.)*

Directions: Survey five people. Ask them to tell you their three favorite animals and their three favorite plants. List each in order of preference. Be sure to record the person's name.

Name	Favorite Animals	Favorite Plants
	1. 2. 3.	1. 2. 3.
Name	**Favorite Animals**	**Favorite Plants**
	1. 2. 3.	1. 2. 3.
Name	**Favorite Animals**	**Favorite Plants**
	1. 2. 3.	1. 2. 3.
Name	**Favorite Animals**	**Favorite Plants**
	1. 2. 3.	1. 2. 3.
Name	**Favorite Animals**	**Favorite Plants**
	1. 2. 3.	1. 2. 3.

Let's Take a Survey *(cont.)*

Answer these questions based on the results of your group's surveys. Use your group graph to help you.

What were your group's top three favorite animals?

_____

_____

_____

What were your group's top three favorite plants?

_____

_____

_____

Did people have an easier time listing their favorite plants or favorite animals?

Of the favorite animals on your graph...

how many are primary consumers? _____

how many are secondary consumers? _____

how many are top consumers? _____

Of the top six favorite animals...

how many can you find in your neighborhood? _____

how many would you have to travel to another state to see? _____

how many live in water for most of their lives? _____

how many live on land for most of their lives? _____

Of the top six favorite plants...

how many could be found in your neighborhood? _____

how many would you have to travel to another state to see? _____

how many are water plants? _____

how many are land plants? _____

Ecosystem Challenge

Question

How are people impacting our local ecosystem?

Setting the Stage

- Have students think about their favorite park or nature center in their community. Then have them brainstorm a list of things in that ecosystem that make it appealing. (For example: It has bluebirds, there is a creek in the park that is good for fishing, etc.)
- Review with students the list and pick the top five most important features of that ecosystem.

Materials Needed for Each Student

- clipboard
- pencil
- data-capture sheet (page 68)

Procedure

1. Take your class on a trip to the park or nature center.
2. Break the class into smaller groups of students. Assign an adult to each of these small groups.
3. The groups should then take their data-capture sheets and walk for 30 minutes. Each time they see one of the challenges listed on the data-capture sheet, they should make a tally mark next to it.
4. After 30 minutes of walking, the students should total their tally marks.
5. Small groups should then share their results with each other.
6. Discuss as a class how each of the things listed could impact the plants, animals, soil, and water of the ecosystem.

Extensions

- Have students survey the local newspapers for articles about challenges to local parks, nature centers, or open countryside.
- Invite a park manager or nature center director to speak to your class about challenges they have in defending the ecosystem.

Closure

In their ecology journals, have students brainstorm a list of ways to educate others about the human impact on parks—for example, poster campaigns, skits, letters to the editor, letters to government officials, etc. Plan a strategy and implement one of the suggestions.

Ecosystem Challenge *(cont.)*

Directions: Your group will be walking for 30 minutes. Read through the list so that you are familiar with it. As you are walking, each time you see one of these items, put a tally mark by it. Total up your tally marks at the end of the walk. (You may want to bring a plastic bag and pick up the litter rather than just leaving it).

Challenge	Tally	Total
pieces of litter		
erosion due to human disturbance		
bare soil due to human impact		
damaged bark or trees (tree carvings included)		
muddy creek or stream water		
signs or presence of domestic animals		

Threatened or Endangered

Question

What are *threatened* and *endangered species?*

Setting the Stage

Review the words *niche, habitat*, and *population*. Ask the students to give examples of each.

Materials Needed for the Class

- a variety of craft supplies: clay, pipe cleaners, sticks, glue, staples, paper, tissue paper, toothpicks, tape, scrap materials, straws, etc.
- data-capture sheet (page 70), one per student

Procedure

1. Ask each child to make a model of a make-believe creature. The model must include adaptations that will help the animal survive, allow it to capture its food, etc..

2. Once they have completed the models, they should answer the questions on the data-capture sheet.

3. Students should then share their creatures with their classmates, basing their explanations on the responses they gave on their data-capture sheets.

4. Ask students to trade creatures and data-capture sheets. Everyone should have another person's creature.

5. Each person should then list things that might harm this creature, based on its habitat description, food requirements, and niche. Students should record these harmful things on the bottom section of their data-capture sheets. Have them use the back of the sheet if they need more room.

6. As a group, share some of the things that could harm the creatures. Are there any things on the list that could threaten an entire population of those creatures? List those separately on the board.

Extensions

- Have students research an endangered species, its habitat, food, and niche. Describe how it has become endangered and what is being done to protect it.
- Have students write local and national officials to ask the status of the endangered species act in your state and in the country.
- Have students write national environmental organizations requesting information on what can be done to protect threatened or endangered species in your area.

Closure

In their ecology journals, have students brainstorm a list of species that they know are threatened or endangered. Then have them make a list of ways that these animals could be protected.

Threatened or Endangered *(cont.)*

Fill in the information needed.

Creature Name _____

1. Describe this creature's habitat and tell where it is found in the world.

2. Describe what and how this animal eats.

   Is it a herbivore, carnivore, or omnivore?

   Is it a primary, secondary, or top consumer?

3. Name what might eat this animal.

4. Describe adaptations your creature has for protecting itself. (Think about the time of day it is active, whether it is a loner or community animal, etc.)

This section will be completed by a classmate.

Student Name _____

What may be harmful to this creature?

70

Who Needs a Tree?

Question

How do people depend on a forest?

Setting the Stage

Have students survey books or go outside and draw pictures of trees. Use the pictures to help answer the following questions:

What are the essential parts of a tree?

What are some different types of trees?

What are some growth requirements of trees?

Materials Needed for Entire Class

- large tree branch
- pot or stand to hold the branch up
- construction paper
- scissors
- string
- glue
- tape
- magazines, newspapers, and advertisements to cut up
- data-capture sheet (page 72), one per student

Procedure

1. Have students each find and cut out 3-5 pictures of things that come from trees.
2. Have students glue the pictures onto construction paper and trim around the edges.
3. Have students attach string to the back of the pictures.
4. Allow students to hang pictures on the tree branch. The tree branch is now decorated with all the different products that come from trees.
5. Look back at the list the students created at the beginning of the experience. Do they wish to add anything?
6. Draw a picture of the tree your group has created on your data-capture sheet.

Extensions

- Invite a forester to speak to the class about timber management.
- Take students to visit a tree farm or nursery. Tour the area and learn about the care that is needed to maintain the area.
- Have students make a map of the National Forests in the United States.

Closure

In their ecology journals, have students list 15 products that come from trees, putting a star by five things that they could not manage without and a check by five things they could manage without. Share these lists. What are the priorities of the class? How might these differ for other people?

Who Needs a Tree? *(cont.)*

Draw a picture of the class tree.

Development Craze

Question

How does development impact an ecosystem?

Setting the Stage

Review carrying capacity, page 34 (See activity page 80.)

Materials Needed for Each Class

- basketball court
- 25 foot (8 m) rope
- one piece of playground equipment per student (e.g., jump ropes, balls, bean bag launchers)
- data-capture sheet (page 76), one per student

Procedure

1. Spread enough playground equipment around the basketball court so that every student will have something to play with. Lay the rope across one end of the basketball court.
2. Explain to students that the basketball court is an ecosystem and that they are going to be the animals living in that ecosystem. The playground equipment will represent food sources.
3. Have students play with the equipment, not removing it from the spot they found it. Have them note the size of the ecosystem and the number of animals and food sources each time they play. Have them record this information on their data-capture sheets.
4. After students have been playing for a few minutes, move the rope, with the help of a volunteer, into the court. You should block off a quarter of the court. The blocked-off area represents the newly developed land. The animals are allowed to move into the remaining area, but they can not take the food sources with them because they have been destroyed by the development.
5. Have students resume play.
6. After students have been playing for a few minutes, move the rope to the middle of the court.
7. Repeat this process until only a quarter of the ecosystem remains.
8. Complete your data-capture sheet.

Extensions

- Have students write local developers about the impact they have on ecosystems. Ask how they might support impacted ecosystems.
- Have students write local government officials about the importance of preserving ecosystems.

Closure

In their ecology journals, have students make a list of other effects of development.

Development Craze *(cont.)*

Size of Ecosystem 1 _____

Number of Animals _____

Number of Food Sources _____

Size of Ecosystem 2 _____

Number of Animals _____

Number of Food Sources _____

Size of Ecosystem 3 _____

Number of Animals _____

Number of Food Sources _____

Size of Ecosystem 4 _____

Number of Animals _____

Number of Food Sources _____

How did development affect the ecosystem?

_____

_____

How did development affect the animals?

_____

_____

How did development affect the food sources?

_____

_____

Language Arts

Reading, writing, listening, and speaking experiences blend easily with the teaching and reinforcement of science concepts. In fact, science can be a focal point as you guide your students through poems and stories, stimulating writing assignments, and dramatic oral presentations. If carefully chosen, language arts materials can serve as a springboard to an animal lesson, the lesson itself, or an entertaining review.

There is a wealth of good literature to help you connect your curriculum. Some excellent choices are suggested in the Bibliography (pages 95-96).

Science Concept: *the complexity of food chains*

Read *Over the Steamy Swamp* (Harcourt Brace Jovanovich, 1988) to your class. Have volunteers retell the story using pictures of the characters. Discuss how food chains work. Help your class create a food chain of their own. Have students write a class big book based on their food chain. Students may also choose to create their own food chains and display them as mobiles.

Science Concept: *helping the environment*

If weather permits, take your class outside to a comfortable spot. Brainstorm and record ways to help the environment with your class. Read *It's My Earth, Too* (Doubleday, 1992) to the class. Discuss the book and allow students to add to their list of ways to help the environment. Have students make posters encouraging others to help the environment. Hang the posters around the school. Help students design a pamphlet to be sent home that encourages environmentally aware actions. As a class, choose at least two things on the list to do at school.

Science Concept: *ecosystems*

Talk about different ecosystems (e.g. deserts, mountains, oceans, plains, swamps, tundra, etc.) with your class. Read them a description of an ecosystem, such as *Mojave* (Thomas Y. Crowell, 1988) or *Sierra* (Harper Collins, 1991). List the elements of the ecosystem described. Ask your class to describe the ecosystem in which they live and to list its elements. Have students write their own descriptions of the local ecosystem. Create a class mural of the ecosystem in which they live. Display their descriptions around the edges of the mural.

Social Studies

Ecosystems have played a significant role throughout history. Civilizations have thrived or declined because of them. Cultures have been built around them, and people have devoted their lives to working with them to make conditions in the world better in some way.

As you guide your students through lessons in history, geography, cultural awareness, or other areas of social studies, keep in mind the role ecosystems have played. You will find it easy to incorporate the teaching and reinforcement of science concepts in your lessons.

Science Concept: *ecological awareness*

Ask students to bring in articles about ecological issues from newspapers and magazines. Share these articles with the class. Post them on a bulletin board with a world map, indicating where each occurred. Help the students to write and publish their own newspaper about ecological issues.

Science Concept: *niches*

Review the meaning of niche with your class. Ask them what some of the niches are that animals fill. Explain that people have niches too. Ask the class what niches they think people fill. List the different niches and who fills them. Use this opportunity to discuss community helpers and careers. Ask students what niche they want to fill when they become adults. Have students write a short description of that niche and draw a picture of themselves filling it. Attach the descriptions to the pictures and display them.

Science Concept: *respecting the environment*

Read *Brother Eagle, Sister Sky* by Susan Jeffers (Dial Books, 1991) to your class. Discuss how the Native Americans felt about the environment. Discuss how people feel about the environment today. Compare the feelings of the Native Americans to the feelings of people today. Have students brainstorm ways of encouraging people to respect the environment, and have them choose one approach to try themselves.

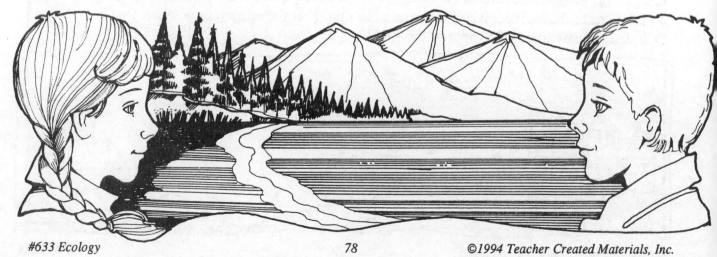

Math

The study of animals requires the use of math skills. Measuring, comparing, and graphing are just a few of the skills that can bring mathematics into your animal lessons.

- Teach or review the use of measuring tools (such as rulers with centimeters and inches to measure length).
- Have students practice reading and making charts and graphs.
- Provide opportunities for students to record data on a variety of graphs and charts. Teach the skills necessary for success.
- Encourage students to devise their own ways to show the data they have gathered.
- On an appropriate level, teach how to average test results.
- Challenge students to find mathematical connections as they study animals.

Science Concept: *endangered animals*

Read a book about endangered animals. (See bibliography for suggestions.) Talk about the different animals which are endangered and why. Make a class counting book using endangered animals. Here is a format idea: There are many wonderful animals in the world, but what will we do when there are only ten giant pandas left? What will we do when there are only nine manatees left? Will we be sorry we did not do anything sooner?

Science Concept: *conservation of natural resources*

Brainstorm the natural resources that the class uses on a daily basis (water, trees, gas, etc.). Ask the students how they can help conserve these resources. Have the students conduct a survey of at least ten people on whether or not they make efforts to conserve (turn off the water when brushing teeth, use cloth towels, carpool, etc.). Students can then use the information collected to create simple bar graphs of their results.

Physical Education

What can be more fun for primary students then imagining they are part of an ecosystem, subject to the forces that make ecosystems grow, thrive, and move? Here is an opportunity to let your students develop their knowledge of ecosystems in a physical way.

Science Concept: *the interdependence of all things in an ecosystem*

Have students stand front-to-back in a very tight circle, all facing one direction. The goal is to have everyone sit down on the knees of the person behind, without falling down. Instruct the students to sit on the count of three. Give it a try. With practice the class should be able to sit on one another's knees without the circle collapsing. Warn students to be still while sitting, as their movements will affect the rest of their classmates, just as changes in one part of the ecosystem can disrupt the entire ecosystem. Remove one of the students while the group is sitting. What happens? This is what happens when part of an ecosystem is removed.

Science Concept: *carrying capacity*

Draw a 4' x 6' (1.2 m x 1.8 m) rectangle on the playground with chalk. Tell your class that this is the ecosystem and they are the various plants and animals that live there. Have three students sit in the rectangle. Is there enough room for them? Have three more students sit in the rectangle. Is it as comfortable as it was before? Keep adding students to the rectangle until it can no longer hold anyone. How many students can the rectangle hold? This is the carrying capacity of the ecosystem. Explain to students what carrying capacity means. Ask them what factors, besides size, may affect the carrying capacity of an ecosystem (food and water availability).

80

Art

Art projects using ecosystems abound in the school and home. Your students will enjoy the "ecosystem possibilities."

Science Concept: *elements of an ecosystem*

Have each student choose an ecosystem for which to create a collage. Students should look for pictures of things found in their ecosystem in magazines, advertisements, and newspapers. After finding a picture, students may cut or carefully tear it out. Once a variety of things have been found, students can glue them onto construction paper, creating an informational collage about their ecosystem. Remember to label the collages so that others will know which ecosystem it represents. (A variation on this would be to create a collage of things that harm the environment.)

Music

Singing songs about ecosystems, selecting orchestral numbers to "promote" the importance of ecosystems, and making sounds that occur in different ecosystems are just a few of the ways to integrate music into your ecosystem-based lessons.

Science Concept: *sounds of an ecosystem*

Let your students find a comfortable place on the floor. Tell them that you are going to turn out the lights and that you want them to close their eyes, stay very still, and listen. Turn off the lights and play an environmental tape of an ecosystem (ocean, jungle, field, etc.) for your class. (Try to find one that does not include instrumentals.) After about five minutes, stop the tape, turn on the lights, and have the students open their eyes. Ask them to describe the sounds that they heard. What do they think the sounds were? What kind of ecosystem were they listening to? Have them describe what they pictured the ecosystem to be like.

82

Science Safety

Discuss the necessity for science safety rules. Reinforce the rules on this page or adapt them to meet the needs of your classroom. You may wish to reproduce the rules for each student or post them in the classroom.

1. Begin science activities only after all directions have been given.

2. Never put anything in your mouth unless it is required by the science experience.

3. Always wear safety goggles when participating in any lab experience.

4. Dispose of waste and recyclables in proper containers.

5. Follow classroom rules of behavior while participating in science experiences.

6. Review your basic class safety rules every time you conduct a science experience.

You can still have fun and be safe at the same time!

Ecology Journal

Ecology Journals are an effective way to integrate science and language arts. Students are to record their observations, thoughts, and questions about past science experiences in a journal to be kept in the science area. The observations may be recorded in sentences or sketches which keep track of changes both in the science item or in the thoughts and discussions of the students.

Ecology Journal entries can be completed as a team effort or an individual activity. Be sure to model the making and recording of observations several times when introducing the journals to the science area.

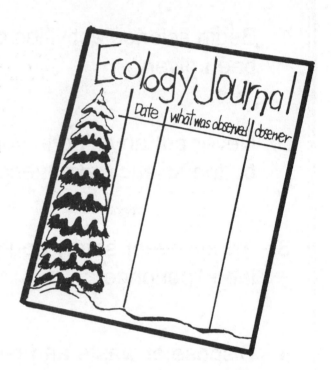

Use the student recordings in the Ecology Journal as a focus for class science discussions. You should lead these discussions and guide students with probing questions, but it is usually not necessary for you to give any explanation. Students come to accurate conclusions as a result of classmates' comments and your questioning. Ecology Journals can also become part of the students' portfolios and overall assessment program. Journals are a valuable assessment tool for parent and student conferences as well.

How To Make a Ecology Journal

1. Cut two pieces of 8 ½" x 11" (22 cm x 28 cm) construction paper to create a cover. Reproduce page 85 and glue it to the front cover of the journal. Allow students to draw plant pictures in the box on the cover.
2. Insert several Ecology Journal pages. (See page 86.)
3. Staple together and cover stapled edge with book tape.

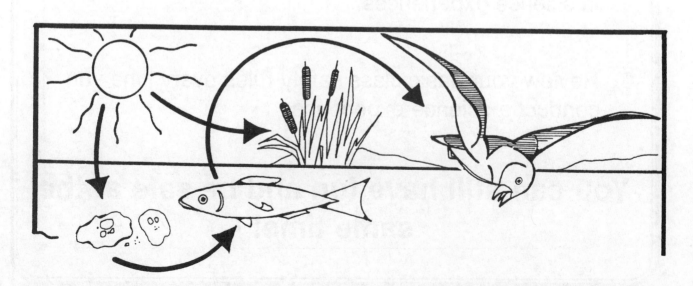

My Ecology Journal

Name_____

Ecology Journal

Illustration

This is what happened: _____

_____

_____

_____

_____

This is what I learned: _____

_____

_____

_____

_____

Investigation Planner

Observation

_____

_____

Question

_____

_____

Hypothesis

_____

_____

Procedure

Materials Needed:

_____

_____

_____

Step-by-Step Directions: (Number each step!)

_____

_____

_____

_____

_____

Ecology Observation Area

In addition to station-to-station activities, students should be given other opportunities for real-life science experiences. For example, terrarium and habitat samples can provide vehicles for discovery learning if students are given time and space to observe them.

Set up a ecology observation area in your classroom. As children visit this area during open work time, expect to hear stimulating conversations and questions among them. Encourage their curiosity but respect their independence!

Books with facts pertinent to the subject, item, or process being observed should be provided for students who are ready to research more sophisticated information.

Sometimes it is very stimulating to set up a science experience or add something interesting to the Ecology Observation Area without a comment from you at all! If the experiment or materials in the observation area should not be disturbed, reinforce with students the need to observe without touching or picking up.

Assessment Forms

The following chart can be used by the teacher to rate cooperative-learning groups in a variety of settings.

Science Groups Evaluation Sheet

Room: _____   Date: _____

Activity: _____

Everyone	Group									
	1	2	3	4	5	6	7	8	9	10
. . . gets started.										
. . . participates.										
. . . knows jobs.										
. . . solves group problems.										
. . . cooperates.										
. . . keeps noise down.										
. . . encourages others.										

Teacher comment

_____

Bragging rights for the group session: _____

_____

         #633 Ecology

Assessment Forms *(cont.)*

The evaluation form below provides student groups with the opportunity to evaluate the group's overall success.

Cooperative Group Evaluation

Assignment: _____

Date: _____

Scientists	Jobs
_____	_____
_____	_____
_____	_____

As a group, decide which face you should fill in and complete the remaining sentences.

1. We finished our assignment on time, and we did a good job.

2. We encouraged each other, and we cooperated with each other.

3. We did best at _____

_____ .

4. Next time we could improve at _____

_____ .

90

Assessment Forms *(cont.)*

The following form may be used as part of the assessment process for hands-on science experiences.

Science Anecdotal Record Form

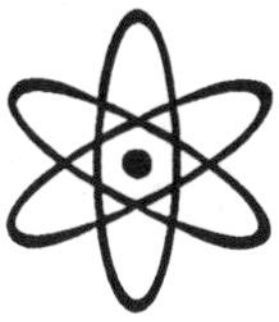

Date: _____

Scientist's Name: _____

Topic: _____

Assessment Situation: _____

Instructional Task: _____

Behavior/Skill Observed: _____

_____

_____

_____

_____

_____

This behavior/skill is important because _____

_____

_____

_____

_____

_____ .

Super Ecologist Award

This is to certify that

_____

Name

made a science discovery!

Congratulations!

_____

Teacher

_____

Date

Glossary

Carnivore—an animal that eats the meat of other animals to survive.

Carrying Capacity—the greatest number of organisms an environment can support.

Community—the interacting plants and animals of a habitat.

Conclusion—the outcome of an investigation.

Condensation—the process by which a gas becomes a liquid.

Consume—to eat or drink.

Consumer—an animal that relies on producers or other consumers for food.

Cycle—an interval of time that is regularly repeated.

Decompose—to break down into component parts.

Decomposer—an organism which converts dead organic materials into inorganic materials.

Ecologist—a scientist who studies the interaction among living things and their environment.

Ecology—the study of the relationship among living organisms and their environment.

Ecosystem—the combination of all living things in a community and its nonliving, or physical environment.

Endangered Species—a species that is in danger of becoming extinct.

Environment—all that is external to the living body of an organism.

Evaporation—the process by which a liquid becomes a gas.

Experiment—a means of proving or disproving a hypothesis.

Food Chain—the relationship between plants and animals by which food energy is transferred by being consumed.

Germination—the sprouting of new life from a seed.

Habitat—the environment in which a plant or animal can naturally be found.

Herbivore—an animal that eats plants in order to survive.

Hypothesis (hi-POTH-e-sis)—an educated guess to a question you are trying to answer.

Impact—to affect strongly.

Interdependent—depending on or needing one another.

Investigation—an observation of something followed by a systematic inquiry to examine what was originally observed.

Niche—the role an organism plays in an ecosystem.

Observation—careful notice or examination of something.

Omnivore—an animal that eats both plants and animals in order to survive.

Population—the number of organisms in a specified area.

Glossary *(cont.)*

Precipitation—condensed water vapor that falls as rain, hail, or snow.

Predator—an animal that hunts and eats other animals.

Prey—an animal that is hunted and eaten by other animals.

Primary Consumer—an animal that eats a producer.

Procedure—the series of steps carried out in an experiment.

Producer—a green plant able to make its own food using energy from the sun.

Question—a formal way of inquiring about a particular topic.

Results—the data collected after an experiment.

Run-off—water that is not absorbed into the soil but runs into another body of water.

Scavenger—an animal that does not kill its own food, but eats what is left of a dead animal or plant.

Scientific Method—a creative and systematic process of proving or disproving a given question, following an observation. Observation, question, hypothesis, procedure, results, conclusion, and future investigations comprise the scientific method.

Scientific-Process Skills—the skills needed to think critically. Process skills include: observing, communicating, comparing, ordering, categorizing, relating, inferring, and applying.

Secondary Consumer—an animal which eats other consumers, but in turn is also eaten.

Threatened Species—a species likely to become extinct due to a decrease in population.

Top Consumer—an animal that eats other consumers, but is not itself eaten by other consumers.

Variable—the changing factor of an experiment.

Bibliography

Asimov, Isaac. *Where Does Garbage Go?* Gareth Stevens, Inc., 1992.

Bowden, Joan. *Where Does Our Garbage Go?* Doubleday, 1992.

Breiter, Herta S. *Pollution.* Raintree LB, 1987.

Bright, Michael. *Pollution & Wildlife.* Watts, 1992.

    Polluting the Oceans. Watts, 1991.

Burnie, David. *How Nature Works.* Dorling & Kindersley, 1991.

Caduto, Michael and Joseph Bruchac. *Keepers of the Animals.* Fulcrum, Inc., 1989.

Caduto, Michael and Joseph Bruchac. *Keepers of the Earth.* Fulcrum, Inc., 1988.

Carson, Rachel. *The Sense of Wonder.* Harper & Row, 1965.

Cherry, Lynne. *The Great Kapok Tree.* Harcourt, Brace & Company, 1990.

Corson, Walter H. *The Global Ecology Handbook.* Global Tomorrow Coalition. Beacon Press, 1990.

Cowcher, Helen. *Rain Forest.* Farrar, Straus and Giroux, 1988.

Docekal, Eileen M. *Nature Detective—How to Solve Outdoor Mysteries.* Sterling Publishing, 1989.

Durrell, Gerald. *Amateur Naturalist.* Alfred Knopf, 1992.

Earthworks Group. *50 Simple Things Kids Can Do to Save the Earth.* Andrews and McMeel, 1990.

Earthworks Group. *Kid Heroes of the Environment.* Andrews and McMeel, 1992.

Geraghty, Paul. *Over the Steamy Swamp.* Harcourt Brace Jovanovich, Inc. 1988.

Glimmerveen, Ulco. *A Tale of Antarctica.* Scholastic, 1989.

Holmes, Anita. *A Kid's Handbook for Keeping Earth Healthy and Green...I Can Save the Earth.*
    Simon and Schuster, 1993.

Jeffers, Susan and Chief Seattle. *Brother Eagle, Sister Sky.* Dial Books, 1991.

Krull, Kathleen. *It's My Earth, Too: How I Can Help the Earth Stay Alive.* Doubleday, 1992.

Lambert, David. *Pollution & Conservation.* Silver Burdett Pr., 1989.

Levine, Shar and Allison Grafton. *Projects for a Healthy Planet.* John Wiley and Sons, 1992.

Lovett, Sarah. *Extremely Weird Endangered Species.* John Muir Publications, 1992.

Lye, Keith. *Our Planet Earth.* Random Books Young Reader, 1993.

Madden, Don. *The Wartville Wizard.* Macmillan, 1993.

Madgwick, Wendy. *Animaze—A Collection of Amazing Nature Mazes.* Alfred Knopf, 1992.

Marshak, Suzanna. *I Am the Ocean.* Arcade Publishing, 1991.

McKvey, Vicki. *Sierra Club Kid's Guide to Planet Care and Repair.* Sierra Club, 1993.

McLain, Gary. *The Indian Way—Learning to Communicate with Mother Earth.*
    John Muir Publications, 1990.

McLaughlin, Molly. *Earthworms, Dirt & Rotten Leaves: An Exploration in Ecology.*
    Macmillan, 1986.

Miles, Betty. *Save the Earth! An Ecology Handbook for Kids.* Knopf, 1974.

Parker, Steve. *Random House Book of How Nature Works.* Random Books for Young Readers, 1993.

Peak, Jan & Anna Henning. *Trash to Treasure Crafts: From Recyclable Materials.* Standard
    Pub., 1992.

Rothman, Joel. *Once There Was a Stream.* Scroll Pr., 1973.

Saven, Beth. *Earthwatch—Earthcycles and Ecosystems.* Addison-Wesley, 1991.

Bibliography *(cont.)*

Showers, Paul. *Where Does the Garbage Go?* Harper LB, 1974.

Siebert, Diane. *Mojave.* Thomas Y. Crowell, 1988.

Siebert, Diane. *Sierra.* HarperCollins, 1991.

Spurgeon, Rich. *Usborne Science and Experiments: Ecology.* Usborne Publishing, 1988.

Stone, Lynn M. *Endangered Animals.* Childrens Press, 1984.

Stone, Lynn M. *Marshes & Swamps.* Childrens Press, 1983.

Van Cleaves, Janice. *Mind Boggling Experiments You Can Turn Into Science Fair Projects: Animals.* John Wiley and Sons, 1993.

Whitfield, Philip. *Can the Whales Be Saved? Questions about the Natural World & the Threats to Its Survival Answered by the Natural History Museum.* Penguin USA, 1989.

Wilcox, Charlotte. *TRASH!* Walker LB, 1988.

Spanish Titles

Cowcher, H. *Antartida (Antarctica).* Farrar, Strauss & Giroux, 1993.

Sendak, M. *Donde viven los monstruos (Where the Wild Things Are).* Santillana Pub. Co., 1993.

Seuss. *El Lorax (The Lorax).* Lectorum, 1993.

Willow, D. *Dentro de la selva tropical (At Home in the Rain Forest).* Charlesbridge Publishing, 1992.

Technology

Cornet/MTI Film & Video. *Amazonia.* Available from Cornet/MTI Film & Video, (800)777-8100. video

InView. *A Field Trip to the Rainforest & A Field Trip into the Sea.* Available from Sunburst, (800)321-7511. software

MECC. *Science Inquiry: Life Science.* Available from CDL Software Shop, (800)637-0047. software

Optical Data. *Primary Science Volume 1.* Available from Optical Data, (800)524-2481. laserdisc

Partridge Film & Video, Ltd. *Cactus Desert, Monkey Rain Forest, How Animals Get Ready for Winter, How Animals Live through the Winter, Lily Pad Pond, Alligator Swamp, Rocky Mountain Meadow, Squirrel Woodlands, Why Plants Grow Where They Do, Why Animals Live Where They Do, and Plants and Animals Depend on Each Other.* Available from Cornet/MTI Film & Video, (800)777-8100. videodisc, video

Slim Goodbody Corporation. *The Outside Story.* Available from AIT, (800)457-4509. video

Troll. *Animal Homes and Stories & EcoQuest 1.* Available from Troll, (800)526-5289. software